## Tales From The South West

Edited By Machaela Gavaghan

First published in Great Britain in 2019 by:

Young Writers
Remus House
Coltsfoot Drive
Peterborough
PE2 9BF
Telephone: 01733 890066
Website: www.youngwriters.co.uk


Book Design by Ashley Janson

Softback ISBN 978-1-78988-761-7
Hardback ISBN 978-1-83928-175-4
Printed and bound in the UK by BookPrintingUK
Website: www.bookprintinguk.com
YB0415E

# Foreword

Dear Reader,

You will never guess what I did today! Shall I tell you? Some primary school pupils wrote some diary entries and I got to read them, and they were **excellent!**

They wrote them in school and sent them to us here at Young Writers. We'd given their teachers some bright and funky worksheets to fill in, and some fun and fabulous (and free) resources to help spark ideas and get inspiration flowing.

And it clearly worked because **WOW!!** I can't believe the adventures I've been reading about. Real people, make believe people, dogs and unicorns, even objects like pencils all feature and these diaries all have one thing in common – they are **jam-packed** with imagination!

We live and breathe creativity here at Young Writers – it gives us life! We want to pass our love of the written word onto the next generation and what better way to do that than to celebrate their writing by publishing it in a book!

It sets their work free from homework books and notepads and puts it where it deserves to be – **out in the world!** Each awesome author in this book should be **super proud** of themselves, and now they've got proof of their imagination, their ideas and their creativity in black and white, to look back on in years to come!

Now that I've read all these diaries, I've somehow got to pick some winners! Oh my gosh it's going to be difficult to choose, but I'm going to have **so much fun** doing it!

Bye!

**Machaela**

# Contents

## St Joseph's Catholic School, Malmesbury



## St Nicolas CE Primary School, Downderry



## Stowford School, Ivybridge

The
Diaries

# Dear Diary

On Sunday the 17th of March, I woke up very nervous because it was my orange belt grading day. I had been working really hard for this day to come. We drove to the Dojo in Newton Abbot. We changed into our go's and went into the matted room. First, we had a lesson as a warm-up, this included the basics: kata, oyo and kumite. Then we went into the grading room. I waited patiently in line for my turn. My name was called. I did my basics and kata in front of Renshi John.
When grading was finished, we went into the first room and did some karate drills while they decided who had passed.
After ten minutes, we were called into the grading room. After a few moments, my name was called, the decision had been made. I had done it! I had passed. I was presented with my certificate and belt.

**Ayrton Sharp (6)**
Barton Hill Academy, Torquay

# Dear Diary

On Saturday, I was busy playing 'Crash Team Racing' on my PS1. I was doing really well until I was sucked into the game! Dr Neo Cortex captured Kelly. I had to go on adventure mode to unlock two secret characters. I also had to beat four boss battles. My biggest rival was Pura. I played as my favourite character, Dr Gin, and finished all the races, easy to hard, in first place. I unlocked new maps and finally, the moment you've been waiting for, the Oxide challenge: if they won, they'd get Kelly but if I won, I'd get Kelly and rule this planet.
I raced against Oxide. I had to retry lots.
Finally, I beat him. I rescued Kelly and went back to the real world... I was just daydreaming!

**Harry Rowlands (7)**

Barton Hill Academy, Torquay

# Dear Diary

I went to a beach party with my family and my friends. It was a lovely, sunny day. The waves were crashing against the rocks. The music was playing, everyone was dancing, having lots of fun. We then went swimming in the cold sea. We felt the waves under our bodies. We splashed around laughing. When I looked down into the deep water, I saw a mermaid with a glittery, sparkly tail. I invited her to join us for a picnic on the soft sand. We ate strawberries, oranges and sandwiches and we made sandcastles. We played with the beach ball, we also drank vanilla milkshakes. We found different types of shells and fossils and we made a fairy picture. We packed all our stuff into the car and drove home.

**Mia Marrie (7)**
Barton Hill Academy, Torquay

# Dear Diary

On Saturday, I went to Dartmoor with my family. I had a checklist of things I had to find. I had to find: a big rock, a horse, a cow, a sheep, a person, a dog and a river. When I found them, I had to tick them off and take a picture of them. My daddy would treat me if I found them all. We also had a picnic. We had our picnic next to the river, which was making a lovely, loud, swishing sound. My treat for finding everything on the checklist was a McDonald's. What a good treat it was! I had some chicken nuggets, chips and some Coke. The best part of the day was climbing the rocks. What a good day I had in Dartmoor with my family!

**April Adams (7)**
Barton Hill Academy, Torquay

# Dear Diary

Today, I went to Babbacombe Beach with my daddy. We walked down a long, winding path from the top of the cliff down to the seaside. I loved playing on the rocks and looking for sea creatures. I saw some little orange and white fish and a small, red crab. It was great to climb about on the rocks but I had to be very careful because the seaweed was slippery.
After a while, we had to walk back up the street path to the top, where the car was parked. My legs were very tired so we sat down on a bench and had nice, cold ice cream. It was a great time!

**Tomas Thompson (6)**
Barton Hill Academy, Torquay

# Dear Diary

I had a lovely time with my family. I went to the park and I played on the slide and the climbing frame. I showed Nanna my best dance moves. I had a milkshake and went with my mummy to go shopping. I bought a really nice dress, it had rainbows. I played lots of games and had a dress-up party. I was a mermaid. I had loads of sweets and chocolate. I did some drawing and colouring and I drew outside with chalk. I had a great weekend seeing my family. I am going to see them again in the summer holidays.
Bye for now,
Love Layla.

**Layla Jobling (6)**
Barton Hill Academy, Torquay

# Dear Diary

Today, I woke up really excited because Auntie Alice was coming from Oxford. I couldn't wait to spend the day at the beach with her.
We went to Dawlish Warren for doughnuts and ice cream but when we got there, there was a power cut. There was no electricity to cook the doughnuts and the ice cream was melting. It was okay because the day was saved by the scooter races and trampoline jumping and a very yummy roast dinner. I was sad when it was time for Auntie Alice to go home. I really do hope that she comes back soon.

**Lily-Jo Prior (6)**
Barton Hill Academy, Torquay

# Dear Diary

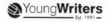

Today we went to Finlake. At Finlake, there are a bunch of water slides. I went on a rainbow slide. I went on a dark blue slide that went really fast. There was a little slide that plunged us down. I also played with Daniel on the slide. We walked around the lake and found some ducks. We fed them with wild bird seeds. They absolutely loved them and flew to us for more. Then we went for a big walk in the forest.
Later on, the trampoline opened. I really enjoyed this weekend with Mum, Daniel, Dad and Fluffy.

**Christopher Csapo (7)**
Barton Hill Academy, Torquay

# Dear Diary

Today, I woke up at 7am because I was so excited about the day. Me, my boyfriend, my best friends, Gabi, Emily, Keely and Sapphire and my family decided to go to a special science museum where we could do our own experiments. Gabi, Emily, Keely and Sapphire had stayed for a sleepover so that we didn't have to pick up five people. We picked up my boyfriend and set off to the science museum.
When we arrived at the museum, we did our own experiments. We looked around and then we all went home.

**Serena Gardiner (7)**
Barton Hill Academy, Torquay

# Dear Diary

I woke up in the morning very early because
I was going to Legoland. It took three hours
to get there.
When we got there, I was very excited.
There were so many rides to check and try.
The most amazing thing about Legoland is
the castle. In Legoland, everything is made
of Lego bricks. I nearly tried all the rides
there! It was a really amazing day.
It was time to go home. We got in the car
and went home.
In the car, I fell asleep.
When we got home, my dad took me to bed.
From Lukas.

**Lukas Arlauskas (7)**
Barton Hill Academy, Torquay

# Dear Diary

I went to the old engine house pub for Mother's Day. My family went: Mummy, Grandad, Clareece, Keelan, Nanny, Danni, Cohen and Great Nanny. Everybody had a carvery roast dinner for lunch. Me, Grandad and Danni had the most amazing ice cream ever but the rest of the family didn't want any.
After that, my cousin was playing with my mum's iPhone, then we had to go so I said bye, but not to Mummy and Grandad because they were coming with me. It was on Sunday the 31st of March.

**Elissia-Mae Greenwood (6)**
Barton Hill Academy, Torquay

# Dear Diary

I was at the beach with Mummy and Daddy. We went to surf and jump over waves, go in the sea, build sandcastles, find shells and rocks and go crabbing. We had a picnic. There were lots of lovely things to eat: sandwiches, fruit and cake. We bought mint chocolate chip ice cream, which is my favourite. I fell into the sea a lot. When the big rocks were hitting me, I fell off my surfboard. I'm getting better at surfing because I learnt a lot when I fell off. I had the best day ever.

**Rio Kaal (7)**
Barton Hill Academy, Torquay

# Dear Diary

As I walked into Bygones, the smell smelt like the queen, really sweet. The queen was sat there very still with a soldier. She was wearing black and blue and looked beautiful. There were lots of things from the olden days. The sweet shop smelt like chocolate fudge. It had dirty, old shoes from a long time ago. The whole place was filled with history. The trench was scary and dark. The best part was seeing the dolls and having hot chocolate with my mum. It was the best day ever.

**Niah Slowley (7)**
Barton Hill Academy, Torquay

# Dear Diary

Today we went to Finlake. We went swimming, I went down the water slides lots of times.
After we had finished swimming, we went on an adventure around the lake and forest. As we were walking around the forest, we spotted a fairy garden. We read a sign saying there was a troll in the forest that had been turned into a statue. Me and my cousin walked barefooted along the muddy trail, our feet were very muddy.
I enjoyed Finlake and I can't wait to go again.

**Oaklie James Chancellor (6)**
Barton Hill Academy, Torquay

# Dear Diary

I went to the pet store and bought a lizard. It kept growing and growing and it was really a dragon!
The next day, I took it to school to show everyone but I forgot to feed it. The dragon was so hungry it ate the whole school, just leaving behind the teachers, the children and a hundred whiteboards! The dragon said that the children could go to the funfair for the whole year but the teachers had to stay behind and do boring education tests on the whiteboards.

**Aydin Ismail Cay (6)**
Barton Hill Academy, Torquay

# Dear Diary

Today, I went out with my loving, beautiful and understanding family. I went to the park and it was epic. I had the best day of my life thanks to my family. I went on the swings and on the slide with my stepbrother. The slide was my favourite colour, it was blue and the swing was orange. The drawbridge was brown.
Next, I had a scrummy picnic, then I went home and watched a scary movie. Then I went to my cosy bed and had a lovely dream.

**Elena Gilbert (6)**
Barton Hill Academy, Torquay

# Dear Diary

First, I went to the zoo with my family. At the zoo, there were some tigers, giraffes, lions and zebras. We also saw some playgrounds. I went to the zoo shop. We ate ice cream, snacks and burgers. We played catch with my grandma. Then we went to the park. I played football with my friends called Mason and Oliver, then we slid down. We also played tag. We did some racing, ate chocolate and drank milkshakes. We had great fun at the park.

**Muhammad Mujtaba Ali (7)**
Barton Hill Academy, Torquay

# Dear Diary

Today, when I was eating lunch at school, I saw a real-life dinosaur and a queen trying to kiss it wearing beautiful clothes. The dinosaur was a robot drone. He was tiny, the same size as my shoe. The queen was little too because it was Tiny Land. The whole school came to Tiny Land and the building then disappeared in a puff! Then the magical, flying school bus came past to visit the clouds and saw us waiting to get back home!

**Viktor Chamberlain-Drury (7)**
Barton Hill Academy, Torquay

# Dear Diary

I went to the funfair with a unicorn and we had lots of fun, that's why it's called a funfair. We played for a bit, then we got some cake and ice cream. We explored the funfair and went on some rides. We went on the teacups. We were very sleepy so we stayed at a hotel for the night.
The next morning, we left. We watched a movie. We ate some popcorn and chocolate, then we went to bed after brushing our teeth.

**Violet May Dowdall (7)**
Barton Hill Academy, Torquay

# Dear Diary

Today, I have been on a trip to the park in Goodrington. We played gymnastic fairies. James didn't want to play because he doesn't like fairies and girl stuff. He only likes cars and motorbikes.
Next, we went to the funfair. Dad didn't want to come because he was too tired. I won a really big unicorn teddy from my coconut throw because I got three in a row!

**Emily-Daisy Burkitt (6)**
Barton Hill Academy, Torquay

# Dear Diary

Today I went to catch Pokémon like Blastoise, Mew Clove, Scyther and Popplio with a monster who had ten eyes, eight legs, twenty arms and three heads! The monster helped me catch my Pokémon. After, we had a Pokémon battle. We had to choose two Pokémon. He chose Blastoise and Charizard. I chose Dark Mewtwo. After, we had a picnic.

**Kane Corbitt (7)**
Barton Hill Academy, Torquay

# Dear Diary

Today I had the most magical day with my pretend unicorn. She likes slime and she likes water. Her name is Disibee, she is colourful and sparkly. She has sparkly colours like pink, purple and gold stripes with a rainbow mane. My unicorn likes sparkles and she likes sausages.

**Billie-Jo Dolling (7)**
Barton Hill Academy, Torquay

# Dear Diary

After school on Friday, Daddy took me and Frankie to the park. I played on the swing. I played on the zip line and the slide. I made a secret shortcut through the wall, up the road. I liked that it was sunny so I didn't need to wear my coat.

**Bella Metcalfe (7)**
Barton Hill Academy, Torquay

# Dear Diary

Today, I made a cake with my sister. We decorated it together. Me and my sister and my mummy went to the park after school and played on the swings, in the sand, and we had some doughnuts.

**Bobby Matthews (6)**
Barton Hill Academy, Torquay

# Dear Diary

Yesterday I went to go to town but the bus was late so I went to McDonald's.
After, I went to the shops to look around. I had so much fun.
Later, I went home.

**Aaliyah Akpo (7)**
Barton Hill Academy, Torquay

# Dear Diary

Wow, what an adventure. It all started on Sunday evening. I was in bed with my dog, Max. We were just about to go to sleep when all of a sudden, I heard a noise. I peered out of my duvet and noticed my wall was starting to crack. Then a portal appeared. I couldn't believe my eyes! Me and Max got out of bed and tiptoed over to get a closer look. Suddenly, a whirling gust of wind like a tornado sucked us up. The next thing I knew, we were in a jungle with colourful birds flying around us. Suddenly, a loud cry noise echoed through the jungle. The noise got closer until a strange creature popped out of the bushes. It looked like it was in pain. As I tried to calm it down, I realised it was a woofabug. "Wow, these are rare creatures," I said to Max. We needed to help him and find our way home!

We walked back to where we had landed. Another tornado appeared and quickly, me, Max and the woofabug jumped in.
A few seconds later, we were very happy to land back in my bedroom. I hid the woofabug under my bed until the morning. That's when Mum came in and noticed him. But guess what? She let me keep him! From that day on I've had two best friends: Max and the woofabug, and we have lots of adventures!

**Isaac Holt (7)**
Bishop Cornish CE (VA) Primary School, Saltash

# Dear Diary

Today, I went to the park with my friend. We found a hidden cave so me and my friend, Sam, decided to go into the cave. It was dark and gloomy inside. Sam had his phone with him. He turned on the light. We thought it would lead us to the other side of the cave, however, it led us to a battlefield. We had no idea what to do so we just stood there looking and listening to the crowd. Luckily, I had my toy Poké Ball with me. I didn't know that it had turned into a real one! I felt the ball moving in my pocket so I took it out to see a mini, yellow hand poking out of it. We realised we were on a Pokémon battlefield. My Poké Ball turned into a Master Ball. When I said, "Pikachu, I choose you," he came out. When I looked up, I saw the Ice King battler. The Icy King has really rare ice Pokémon.

We decided to battle him. My Pikachu is really strong and clever in battle, he won against the Ice King. Suddenly, after a flash of light, we were back in the cave. We went back to the park and had a little play before it was time to go home. That was an amazing day!

**Harrison Dark (7)**
Bishop Cornish CE (VA) Primary School, Saltash

# Dear Diary

Monday was a beautiful, sunny day. I, Bella the princess, had a Pokémon called Pretty Tiger. She wore a red bow in her hair and a pink dress with a blue cardigan. Her shoes were red and white.
In the morning, when I was getting ready for princess school, Pretty Tiger whispered in my ear, "Remember, it's mufty day tomorrow."
My school uniform is pink and white stripes. In Year 1 at school, I get to have flying unicorn lessons. We also have jacket potatoes for lunch and chocolate for pudding.
After lunch, there's another unicorn flying lesson, then I can do whatever I want. Then I go home.
Tonight, I read a bedtime story to my three sisters in my triple bunk bed. When I was in

the middle of 'The Very Hungry Caterpillar', they were fast asleep.

**Charlotte Taylor (7)**
Bishop Cornish CE (VA) Primary School, Saltash

# Dear Diary

Today, I went to the funfair with my friends. When we got there, it was lunchtime so we ate candyfloss, sandwiches, crisps and drank Fruit Shoots.
After lunch, we played on the dodgems and then we got our faces painted. I had a unicorn, Katherine had a cat and Charlotte had a butterfly. Then we got some balloons. I had a dog one, Katherine had a butterfly and Charlotte had a unicorn.
After all that, we went on the Ferris wheel. Then we slid down the helter-skelter. We played some games and after that, we saw a fairy! She said, "Hello, can I help you?" We said, "Yes." We didn't know where the slushies were.
"Come over." So we rushed over to the slushies and then we left.

**Bryah Crook (6)**
Bishop Cornish CE (VA) Primary School, Saltash

# Dear Diary

Today, I saw a unicorn with my friend, Jess. Jess has white, short hair and likes chocolate and pasta like me. We went to the park, then we hid behind a rock, waiting for the unicorn. But Jess didn't believe in them... Soon, I came up with a very smart idea to put sweets in front of the rock because unicorns love candy! Just then, I heard a rustle in the bushes. Was it the unicorn? I saw a horn poking through the bush, then the creature darted out and ran around. With one look, I could tell it was my dog, Buddy, with my unicorn hairband on again! Me and Jess could not stop laughing. Soon, my sister came through and got him back on the lead. That was the funniest day of our lives and better than seeing a real unicorn!

**Lucia Marie Nickson (7)**
Bishop Cornish CE (VA) Primary School, Saltash

# Dear Diary

Today, I went to the park with my friend. We played football. After that, we went and had milkshakes and chocolate on the bench, then we went to my house.
We went on the trampoline and it felt like we were touching the sky. We went to have lunch, then we went for a walk to the arcade with our mums. We both won the jackpot, I got a new football with some tickets.
When we got back, we played Fortnite on my Xbox. I got twenty-five kills and won. We went to the zoo. We both found a tiger playing with his dad. We went back to my house and had our tea. After, there was a big surprise for me... my friend was sleeping over!

**Matthew Fox (7)**
Bishop Cornish CE (VA) Primary School, Saltash

# Dear Diary

My name is Grace. On Sunday the 24th of February, my brother, Isaac, was christened. All my family from Wales and Cornwall came to the church to celebrate. We sang hymns, which I chose with the vicar. My cousin Freya and I were special helpers. I held Isaac's candle and Freya and I tipped the water into the font.
Afterwards, we went for Sunday lunch and ate Isaac's christening cake. It was yummy. It was a lovely, sunny day. I played outside with my cousins, then everyone went home and the sun went down into his suitcase, packed himself up and went to another place, then we went to bed. We had such a lovely day!

**Grace Davies (7)**
Bishop Cornish CE (VA) Primary School, Saltash

# Dear Diary

I have ten beautiful baby pandas. Five baby boys and five baby girls. Their names are Fred, Brian, Harry, Jake, Jacob, Cutie, Daisy, Pearl, Maud and Mildred. Their daddy is called Kevin and my name is Katie.
That day, the girls wore pretty, pink JoJo bows and dresses. The boys wore dark blue jumpers and a hat.
I was having my lunch when Jake ran away to the hippo enclosure to play hide-and-seek. I found him on a hippo. He jumped into my arms and we went back to the others. We had sloppy joes and chilli and chocolate brownie cake for tea.

**Katherine Taylor (7)**
Bishop Cornish CE (VA) Primary School, Saltash

# Dear Diary

Today, I was playing a video game. I was playing Niall and Darragh. Just then, Niall dug a hole with his legendary pickaxe. Down in the deep tunnel was a monster known as the guardian of the chest. I looked at the map, the tunnel was a long way through and a storm was on its way. We had to move. I told Niall on my headset to move. Just then, my mum told me it was time for tea. I said, "Now?" I saw a bone, we got the monster. We called it Bob.

**Riley Pitcher (7)**
Bishop Cornish CE (VA) Primary School, Saltash

# Dear Diary

I was at the beach. I was making a sandcastle as big as a giraffe. When I was digging the moat, I found a key. I remembered about a story on the news. I took the key and then I went to the secret passage. I went inside and saw Zach sat on a treasure chest. I heard a click. Suddenly, Zach fell off and Isaac popped out with milkshake and sweets. We had a party.

**Ruben Pocock (7)**
Bishop Cornish CE (VA) Primary School, Saltash

# Dear Diary

Today, I saw the craziest thing ever. I went in the car and fell asleep on the way. I was going to my cousin's house.
When I got there, I went upstairs, then I saw a Pokémon playing on computer games and drinking a milkshake!

**Jacob Blair (7)**
Bishop Cornish CE (VA) Primary School, Saltash

# Dear Diary

Today, I went to the funfair. I saw a fairy and Pikachu! Pikachu got stuck in a milkshake. Then he jumped out but he got stuck in a smoothie!

**Amelia Ayley (6)**

Bishop Cornish CE (VA) Primary School, Saltash

# Dear Diary

Yesterday, I went to Unicorn Land with my rainbow unicorn called Sparkle. First, we went to the park and played together. Then we went to ride on a unicorn and we had so much fun.
When we started to walk around. We saw a unicorn café. I stepped inside and everything was unicorn. I was admiring the delicious cakes. Next, I went back to the unicorns and they flew me back. It was the greatest day of my life!
Love, Darcie.

**Darcie Ava Entwistle (6)**
Blandford St Mary CE (VA) Primary School,
Blandford St Mary

# Dear Diary

Yesterday, I went to Unicorn Land and my family went with me. I had to go in the car for five hours!
When I got to Unicorn Land, I saw lots of unicorns. My family let me go on the unicorns, my sister went on a unicorn too. As we were flying, I was admiring the flowers.
After, me and my family went to a restaurant and I had a burger with chips. It was the best day ever!
Love, Gabriella.

**Gabriella Tsankova (6)**
Blandford St Mary CE (VA) Primary School, Blandford St Mary

# Dear Diary

Yesterday, I went to a fossil museum with a sparkling unicorn. First, we looked at the small animal fossil and we saw what looked like a bird. Then we went to look at the dinosaurs. There were swimming dinosaurs and the water was clear but it was freezing cold!
After that, we went to see the leaf-eating dinosaurs. I can't believe I was so close to these dinosaurs!
Love, Bethany.

**Bethany Bishop (6)**
Blandford St Mary CE (VA) Primary School, Blandford St Mary

# Dear Diary

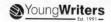

Yesterday was amazing! I went to the funfair. Me and my brother got some sweets. I went on all of the rides with my brother. My mum and dad went on some rides. I was so dizzy I fell over!
I woke up and I saw a boy who was upset. We took him to his mum and dad. We made friends with the nice boy, then went home.

**Lucas Timoney (6)**
Blandford St Mary CE (VA) Primary School, Blandford St Mary

# Dear Diary

Yesterday, I went to Unicorn Land and rode on a golden unicorn! I went to the park with the unicorn. I went on the slide with the unicorn. Next, I went swimming with the unicorn. We went in the big pool together. Next, me and the unicorn went to the sandy beach and we played with a mermaid. It was a good day.

**Kaelia Phillips (6)**
Blandford St Mary CE (VA) Primary School,
Blandford St Mary

# Dear Diary

Yesterday, I had a spectacular dream. A hamster said to me, "We are having a party! I mean, we are having a monster party!" Monsters were there and they danced and danced and danced! We had a hot dog and pizza. We had a Slush Puppie too. It was an incredible dream.
Jack.

**Jack Shipton (6)**
Blandford St Mary CE (VA) Primary School,
Blandford St Mary

# Dear Diary

I went to see the animals with my friends. It was 2 o'clock when we were in the zoo. We saw the parrots squawking and a cheetah running as fast as it could. Then we ate dinner. I was so happy to see all the amazing animals. It was the best ever.
Love, George.

**George Chandler (6)**
Blandford St Mary CE (VA) Primary School,
Blandford St Mary

# Dear Diary

I went to Unicorn Land. I went with a unicorn and it was a rainbow, sparkly unicorn.
When we played, we played with her friends.
In Unicorn Land, we had ice cream. It was fun. We played piggy in the middle. We had an amazing time. Then I went home.

**Isabella Daniels (6)**
Blandford St Mary CE (VA) Primary School,
Blandford St Mary

# Dear Diary

Yesterday, I went to Sweetie Land and it took five minutes to get to Sweetie Land. I ate some of the sweets and Gabriella shared some sweets. It looked amazing. I could see lots of yummy lollipops and chocolate rain.
Love, Jessie.

**Jessie Wheeler (6)**
Blandford St Mary CE (VA) Primary School, Blandford St Mary

# Dear Diary

Yesterday, I went to Unicorn Land with my best friend called Izzy.
When we got there, the unicorn looked good. Me and Izzy followed the pink unicorn and got to play with all her friends. Can you believe it? Then we went home.

**Tegan Rhodes (5)**
Blandford St Mary CE (VA) Primary School, Blandford St Mary

# Dear Diary

Yesterday, I went to Hogwarts and I met Harry Potter. We made potions and played Quidditch. I won six games and Harry won two games. Harry gave me a wand and he taught me all the magic he knew. Then we met Ron and Hermoine. I showed Ron and Hermoine what Harry had taught me. I loved my day at Hogwarts. I hope I can go again. It was so exciting. It was awesome. I loved it! It was so fun.
When I got home, I had a hot chocolate and a biscuit, then I went to bed.
When I woke up this morning, I told my teacher all about my fun adventure.

**Hattie Gooding (6)**
Castle Mead School, Hilperton

# Dear Diary

Last week, I went to the park with my brother called William. I rode my bike all the way and it was very bumpy.
When I got there, I played hide-and-seek for five minutes, then we had a break for some sweets. I played football and William lost. Then William wanted to play hide-and-seek so I decided to go with him. He liked going down the slide. He screamed and it hurt Mummy's ears so Mummy said, "Stop screaming, now!" I can't wait to go again.

**Lily Anderson (5)**
Castle Mead School, Hilperton

# Dear Diary

Last Sunday, I went to the funfair in Ibiza with my friend, Matilda. I could see red flowers and I saw candyfloss. I felt excited, but then I saw a mermaid shaking a milkshake towards a sweetie, glimmering, secret tunnel. Me and Matilda went in it. When we went in it, it was a cave with enchanted crystals glowing everywhere around us!

**Alice Anne Standage (7)**
Castle Mead School, Hilperton

# Dear Diary

Last week, I went to the funfair in Trowbridge with Alba, Alice, Emilija and Beatrix.
When I arrived at the funfair, all I could see was a sign. It made me feel sad because I thought it said it was closed. Then I went to the park. My unicorn said hello to me, then we went home and had a biscuit and a party.

**Isabella Hawker (6)**
Castle Mead School, Hilperton

# Dear Diary

Last week, I went to the funfair with my friend, Lily. It was fun at the funfair. We played for hours. My favourite game was the roller coaster. I couldn't wait to go again. Next time, I will dance with my friend, Lily. It was fun because we played lots of games. I can't wait to go again!

**Imogen Bailey (5)**
Castle Mead School, Hilperton

# Dear Diary

Last week, it was my birthday. I went with a fairy, it was in Fairy Land. I saw lots of fairies. They had long, sparkly wings and soft hair. I played lots of games, my favourite was bingo. In fact, I loved them all. They were all great. The fairies are my BFFs. They danced all night.

**Francesca Rose Lund (6)**
Castle Mead School, Hilperton

# Dear Diary

Today I went to school with Miss Honey, the headmistress is very mean. She is called Miss Trunchbull. Yesterday, I got locked in the chokey but Miss Honey saved me. I felt very sad. Miss Honey felt very worried. Miss Trunchbull was very angry. I don't want to go again.

**Tabitha Trerise (5)**
Castle Mead School, Hilperton

# Dear Diary

Yesterday, I went to school with my BFF, Polly the unicorn. Polly and me read a book together.
After we'd read our book, it was playtime. We played some games. Me and Polly played 'What's The Time, Mr Wolf?' We played very fairly and nicely.

**Evie Millard (7)**
Castle Mead School, Hilperton

# Dear Diary

I went to the safari. I went with Mummy and Daddy. I saw stripy tigers. They scared me a little bit. I also saw spotty cheetahs. They were the fastest. I really enjoyed my day at the safari. I can't wait to go again!

**Marley Strickland (6)**
Castle Mead School, Hilperton

# Dear Diary

I woke up, then I had breakfast. I got into the car and drove to school. I went into my classroom. I was really excited because it was a do-whatever-you-like week. But I didn't know what to do. Then I decided I wanted to do lots of things. First, I played football up the stairs. Some teachers got a little bit angry. Then I gave my monster a number-one monster award. He was smelly! I played computer games for a long time. I played FIFA 10, then I had a big party. There was music and entertainment and lots of lovely food and balloons. I did one more thing, I had a picnic! It was *so* fun! There were lots of things to eat, including the following: sandwiches, crisps, cake and cookies. It was fun.
Bye-bye, write in you later!

**Toby Clennell (7)**
Cheltenham College Prep School, Cheltenham

# Dear Diary

I brushed my teeth so they looked shiny and clean. I was so excited to go to the beach. I went with my two dogs, my monkey, my cat and also with my horses.
When we got there, I leapt off my horse and put them in the stable on the beach. The stable is so cool! Anyway, I ran all the way to the water, then I realised there was nobody on the beach. "This is awesome!" I shouted but then I realised there was a lifeguard so I could do fun things but not dangerous things. I took my clothes off and put my swimsuit on. I ran into this funny thing. I met a mermaid! She made me a mermaid! She told me I'd get my tail every afternoon and I would stop being a mermaid next year. Catch up next time.
Love, Seren.

**Seren Archer (7)**
Cheltenham College Prep School, Cheltenham

# Dear Diary

On Monday, I went to Australia. I went with Matt Simon.
When we arrived, me and Matt Simon drank a delicious smoothie.
After that, we had a party. It was so fun.
Then we had a match. Lots of people came to the match. The match began. First, the score was 1 to Matt Simon, 2 to me. It was a wild match.
After that, the score was 7-5. I was still in the lead. I was zooming down the pitch scoring again and again.
The match was finished. Finally, I had a chocolate ice sorbet. It was a magical adventure. It was time to go home.

**Poppy Charlesworth (6)**
Cheltenham College Prep School, Cheltenham

# Dear Diary

Yesterday was the best day ever! My teddy showed me a world called Toy Land. In Toy Land, toys were free and they were everywhere! I was so amazed.
Next, I bought a massive bag. We put so many toys in the bag. We were so happy. Then we went to an ice cream shop. My teddy had double chocolate. I had mint chocolate chip. Then we rested near the pool. My teddy got sunburnt! I played with a rubber duck. We had so much fun. I didn't want to go home but I had to. I can't wait to go there again!
Bye-bye Diary.

**Archie Oliver Clarke (7)**
Cheltenham College Prep School, Cheltenham

# Dear Diary

Yesterday, I went to a unicorn riding school. I brought my pink, shimmering unicorn. Next, we went to the shiny stables. We had the smallest one. Then we rode a dressage test. It was easy, but then it got harder. It went quiet and everybody was looking at me. Suddenly, I realised that it was my turn. Luckily, I passed and went home. I think I would like to go there again.

**Zandra Elyse Games (7)**
Cheltenham College Prep School, Cheltenham

# Dear Diary

I went to the space centre. I went with Neil Armstrong. We went to the moon. Neil Armstrong told me about when he went. We got to the moon, we found a moon buggy. We drove for a long time.
After a bit, we found a space house, then we had something to eat. Next, we went to explore the moon. I had such a good time. I will tell you some more tomorrow.

**Harry Edgar Cole (6)**
Cheltenham College Prep School, Cheltenham

# Dear Diary

Today, I was so excited because I went to Puppy Land with my family. It was so much fun. We got to play with puppies. We also got to feed newborn puppies.
Finally, we got to go on a special ride with all the puppies in the world, even newborn puppies. I'll write a new entry soon.
Bye Diary.

**Clara Nelson (6)**
Cheltenham College Prep School, Cheltenham

# Dear Diary

Yesterday was the best day because, at Beavers, I got five badges but the good bit was my friend got a bronze badge.
After Beavers, I went to watch my mummy play a netball match. When my mummy finished, she took me to Daddy to have delicious drinks in the people's bar.

**Ludo Conner (7)**
Cheltenham College Prep School, Cheltenham

# Dear Diary

Today was the best day ever! I went to the puppy hotel. They all played together. We got to play with them and hug them.
Finally, I took them for a walk.
I can't wait to go back tomorrow.
Bye-bye Diary, I will write in you again.

**Harriet Louisa Brown (6)**
Cheltenham College Prep School, Cheltenham

# Dear Diary

I had the best day ever. I got out of my cosy bunk bed and looked out of my window. I saw a sparkly unicorn horn and an amazing unicorn wing. I knew that there was a winged unicorn nearby. I slid down the bannister and had my pancakes, got my scout clothes on and went to the forest with my magnifying glass and went to search.
I found a horn with no unicorn! I went exploring and then I found the unicorn.
"Can you please put my horn back on?" it said.
I helped put it on and told it that it could be my pet and then went home with the unicorn.
Love Theiah.

**Theiah Samantha Day (6)**
Cherhill CE Primary School, Cherhill

# Dear Diary

When I woke up this morning, I saw the sun shining in my bedroom window. I threw my gym clothes on and slid down the bannister. I gobbled up my breakfast, it was wonderful and yummy. I threw my gym bag on.
I arrived at the gym. We did some roly-polys and stretches, then it was home time.
When I arrived back at home, I watched TV, then I played with Play-Doh. Here, I write all the happy things.
Love, Lucy.

**Lucy Lindsay**
Cherhill CE Primary School, Cherhill

# Dear Diary

I had the best day ever today. I got up, got dressed and had bread with chocolate spread for breakfast. Then I got in the car and went to the waterfall. I had a little play and then I saw a magical unicorn. The magical unicorn took me to Jester's and I went on the slide. It was fun. I had the best day ever at the weekend. I had lots of fun. Love, Kara.

**Kara Johnson**
Cherhill CE Primary School, Cherhill

# Dear Diary

I had the most awesome day ever. I woke up and looked out of my window. I saw a volcano erupting. I went outside and I saw the poison so I went to Granny and Grampy's house to be safe. I sat there, remembering all the things I'd seen today.
Love, Scarlett.

**Scarlett (6)**
Cherhill CE Primary School, Cherhill

# Dear Diary

I had the best day today. I woke up and saw a unicorn outside my window! I went downstairs. I had breakfast and went outside. There was the unicorn in the snow. He had a sparkling horn. He was so cute. He was also all over the place!
Love, Mia.

**Mia Salmon (5)**
Cherhill CE Primary School, Cherhill

# Dear Diary

I woke up and I smelt some steam. I jumped out of bed. I slid down the bannister for breakfast and I ate faster than a flash. I picked my bag up. I had to go to gymnastics. It was the best day ever.
Love, Kim.

**Kim Gutierrez-Jude (6)**
Cherhill CE Primary School, Cherhill

# Dear Diary

I had the best day ever today. I woke up, I looked out the window and I flew down the stairs. I went to Vampire World! I took my dog and my mum. I am in my coffin as I write this!
Love, Alfie.

**Alfie Murray (6)**
Cherhill CE Primary School, Cherhill

# Dear Diary

I've been to a zoo and a park. I went to a place that was half a zoo, half a playground. When we were there, we played on the trampoline. Then I went to the messy kitchen, I knew Jude would like that. Jude is my friend Evie's baby brother.
In the next playground, I went on the bus and I drove the bus but don't worry, it didn't really move! Then I went on the slide, the big one.
We went for a walk. We walked down the path and then we stopped and saw some cars on the bridge. Then we found where the tennis courts used to be. We had a peek through the gate and saw a statue that was shaped like a horse. After that, we went to the pond. Then we went up the hill, then our cousins arrived so we played on the trampoline and played tag.

After that, we went to the park and fed the llamas. Next, we went on the zip wire. After our lovely day, we went home.

**Annabelle Hodges (6)**
Emersons Green Primary School, Emersons Green

# Dear Diary

Yesterday, I went to a huge island. I saw a flower lady, she had lots of flowers and there was a flower queen. She threw lots of flowers to help her dream about anything. But the funny part was when the caterpillar was tickling my head!
After that, a ladybird trapped me, but I could get out easily. It was such a funny day!

**Oliwia Chocha (6)**
Emersons Green Primary School, Emersons Green

# Dear Diary

Today, I went to LegoLand with my mum, dad, brother and sisters. We made a gigantic Lego car and did a test drive around the world. Then we crashed. What could we do? We had to rebuild it. A perfect idea. We built it and we were off again.

**Youssef Fawzy (6)**
Emersons Green Primary School, Emersons Green

# Dear Diary

Yesterday, I went to after school club and I was playing loads of games.
At the end, when everyone went home, I had a sweetie and chocolate at home. My daddy went to the shops to get some stuff for him and I got some stuff for me.

**Connie Woodman (6)**
Emersons Green Primary School, Emersons Green

# Dear Diary

At the weekend, I went to the zoo. At the zoo, I saw a real lion, a real flamingo, a real lemur and a fish. I had a really fun day, it was really funny when the lion was lying down. It was an amazing day!

**Logan Biddle (5)**
Emersons Green Primary School, Emersons Green

# Dear Diary

Yesterday, I met a unicorn. It was stuck in a tree. I helped it get out. I called my friend, Diddy the dinosaur. He wriggled the tree to make it fall down. I got to take it home. Now it's my pet.

**Penny Ann Bishop (5)**

Emersons Green Primary School, Emersons Green

# Dear Diary

I went to soft play and I met Sophia and Lawson. I went with Violet. Violet hurt her finger on the slide and it was bleeding. A boy threw some balls at me and I cried. He didn't say sorry!

**Charlene Callaghan (6)**
Emersons Green Primary School, Emersons Green

# Dear Diary

At the weekend, I went to cool John's house. I'm staying in a hotel but I went to John's party. It was fun. Then I went for horse training.

**Isabelle Millett (6)**
Emersons Green Primary School, Emersons Green

# Dear Diary

Yesterday, I went to my best friend's birthday party. It was at the cinema. It was so fun. The best part was eating the popcorn!

**Violet Pearce (6)**
Emersons Green Primary School, Emersons Green

# Dear Diary

On Tuesday, I went to Beavers. At Beavers, I saw Harry and I had some pancakes. The most exciting part was eating the pancakes.

**George Willson (6)**
Emersons Green Primary School, Emersons Green

# Dear Diary

Today I was going swimming when I got sucked up by the plug and everyone in the pool was sucked up too! We all ended up in the middle of the ocean! One child was in tears, the parents were stressing out and I was stuck in the middle. Then I heard a loud splashing noise. It was the beautiful sight of dolphins! By the time they got to us, I had a brilliant idea that we could all get on their backs and hopefully, they could take us to shore. So we all got on their backs and they leapt, shot, zoomed and zipped us to shore. When we arrived, we had a crowd cheering that we made it alive. But before we all went home, I gave a big thank you to the dolphins. They happily swam away. I even named one Ellie.

**Elsie Lambert (9)**
Georgeham CE Primary School, Georgeham

# Dear Diary

Today I felt excited because I was going on a school trip to the Somerset Rural Life Museum. Before I got on the bus, I got my packed lunch, then I got on the bus.
When I got to the museum, I sat down and listened to the teacher, Sandy. First of all, we played a game where we had to swipe an object into the correct box, then we split into groups and we did one activity at a time. The first activity we did was putting one hand in a bag. In the bag, there was an object to feel and guess. It was fun!
After that, we had to get a clipboard and a pencil. We also had a piece of paper with boxes and names of materials inside. With our clipboard and pencil, we drew pictures of the museum, then we felt some sheep wool and we had to put soap and water on our hands. We had to make the wool dry by putting it in a paper towel and squishing it down. We looked to see what we'd created. Mine looked like a chick.

After that, I got my packed lunch and ate it.
It was scrummy!
Finally, we had a little booklet all about art.
What a fantastic day I've had!

**Isla Lowdon (6)**
North Newton Community Primary School, North Newton

# Dear Diary

Today, I felt excited because it was our class trip to the Somerset Rural Life Museum. For breakfast, I had five pieces of honey on toast and a lovely, hot glass of milk.
When I got to school, I grabbed my packed lunch and quickly climbed into the big, silver minibus and rocketed to the museum.
Immediately, we had a talk about materials and played a game where we had to drag an object into the box on the Smart Board.
Then my group went into the gallery and drew a picture in the box.
For the next activity, we mixed wool, water and soap and put it in a towel to dry it.
When it came out, it was in the shape of a T-rex! We stuck googly eyes and a magnet to it.
The activity before lunch, we put our hands into a bag with unique bits in it. At half-past one, we had lunch in the orchard. I had a ham wrap, hummus and dips, a yoghurt and

a cake. After lunch, we had a play in the orchard.
Finally, we had to draw a picture of something, I drew a tractor.
When I got home, I brushed my teeth and went to bed. What a lovely day I had!

**Harry Bult (7)**
North Newton Community Primary School, North Newton

# Dear Diary

Today, I felt excited and nervous because it was our amazing class trip to the Somerset Rural Life Museum. I couldn't wait! I had a scrumptious pancake and croissant for breakfast, yum yum!
When I got to school, I got my packed lunch and hopped on the bus. We set off very quickly.
When we got there, we had a talk about what we would do. Sandy, the teacher said, "Shall we play a game on the board?" I got a go! Then we got a clipboard and pencil and went around the museum looking for things we could draw. We were in three groups.
After we'd done, we had lunch. I had an apple, raisins and a sandwich. I almost forgot I had Smarties!
Finally, we got a booklet, it was so much fun! We made up a poem. I read it out with my friend, Daisy.

Before bed, Mum gave me a kiss and a hug.
What a lovely day I had!

**Freya Thomas (7)**
North Newton Community Primary School, North Newton

# Dear Diary

Today, I felt excited because it was our class trip to the Somerset Rural Life Museum. For breakfast, I had scrambled eggs, as usual. When I got to school, I went to the toilet. Quickly, I got my high-vis jacket and grabbed my lunch box and drinks bottle. First, we had a talk with Sandy and played a science game on the Smart Board. Then we made our magnets with Sandy. Next, we looked around the museum and found different materials and felt inside a feely bag.
After that, we had lunch. I had two tuna sandwiches, a yoghurt and a crunchy, red apple.
Finally, we looked around the museum again and learnt about art.
Before bed, I put my magnet on the fridge. What a lovely day I had!

**Charlotte Butler (6)**

North Newton Community Primary School, North Newton

# Dear Diary

Today, I felt excited because I was going on a school trip. For breakfast, I had Coco Pops.
When I got to school, I got my lunchbox and climbed into the silver minibus.
When we got there, we had a talk about different materials. Then we put our hands together and squeezed as hard as we could. Then we had to put our hands in a big bag. Next, we had a clipboard to find some material. After that, we ate lunch in the orchard. I had ham sandwiches and a fruit salad.
After lunch, we took some pictures. I climbed back into the minibus.
Before bed, my mummy kissed me goodnight. What a lovely day. I had an exciting day.

**Bella Davis (6)**

North Newton Community Primary School, North Newton

# Dear Diary

Today, I felt excited because it was my first time at the museum. I had a piece of toast for breakfast, an egg and a glass of orange juice.
When I got to school, I put on my high-vis and went to the toilet.
First, we had a talk and went on the Smart Board. Sandy was nice. Next, we put our hands in a bag to see what material was there and then we went around the museum to find material. We made magnets out of sheep wool.
After that, we had lunch. I had a honey sandwich, salty crisps and a strawberry yoghurt.
Finally, I drew a picture.
Before bed, I had a bath and told Mum all about it. What a good day it was!

**Evellyn Farnham (7)**

North Newton Community Primary School, North Newton

# Dear Diary

Today, I felt excited because it was our class trip to the giant museum!
When I got to school, I jumped out of the silver minibus and zoomed into the giant museum.
A few minutes later, we had a talk about the museum, then I made a sticky fridge magnet and I had to find and draw hard objects on my sheet. Next, I had a feel of the feely bags.
After that, we had lunch, I had crunchy, yummy and hard chocolate.
Finally, I drew a picture of a giant hose, then I jumped into the silver minibus and zoomed back to school.
Before bed, Mummy read me a nice bedtime story. What a lovely day it was!

**Jackson D Mantyk (6)**
North Newton Community Primary School, North Newton

# Dear Diary

Today, I felt happy because it was my first day at the museum. Yay!
When I got to school, I grabbed my lunchbox and jumped on the minibus. First, we had a talk with the museum lady and played a game on the Smart Board. Then we felt stuff in bags. We went into the gallery.
Next, we touched brown sheep wool. After that, we had lunch. I had a brown cake and ham sandwiches with ketchup and cheese too.
Finally, we went back to the minibus and zoomed back to school.
Before bed, I brushed my teeth and washed my hands. I climbed into bed. What a lovely day I had!

**Daniel Phillip Treadwell (6)**
North Newton Community Primary School, North Newton

# Dear Diary

Today, I felt excited because it was our class trip to the Somerset Rural Life Museum. I had raisin wheats for breakfast. I went to school, put on a high-vis and climbed onto the big, silver bus. I read a book on the way. I climbed off the bus and played on the Smart Board, then I made a magnet out of sheep wool and filled in a sheet of paper. I put my hand in a feely bag, then I had a box of raisins and two sandwiches.
After that, I climbed on the bus and went back to school.
Before bed, I watched some TV and climbed into bed. What a lovely day I had!

**Harry Shuttleworth (6)**
North Newton Community Primary School, North Newton

# Dear Diary

Today, I felt excited because it was a sunny day and I had never been to a museum.
When I got to school, I went to the toilet.
Then I got a high-vis jacket and got in the minibus.
When I got there, we had a talk with Sandy, then we played a game on the Smart Board.
I made my magnet. After that, we had a turn to feel inside the bags. We explored the museum, then it was lunchtime. We ate outside. I stroked a horse, then I got my lunchbox, my drinks bottle, my high-vis jacket and zoomed back to school. What a lovely day!

**Gracie Broom (6)**

North Newton Community Primary School, North Newton

# Dear Diary

Today, I felt excited because I went to Butlins for five days and I got a Build-A-Bear with a costume and shoes. It looked so quiet when I got there, but it was really big and busy! I went to a football club. The blue team (my team) won and the red team lost. When it finished, I went to the arcades and got twenty tickets.
At the end of the day, I went back to the bungalow and made a picture of Butlins.
I also went to the arts and crafts centre.
After that, I went to some shows. One of them was very funny!

**Neo Peters (6)**

North Newton Community Primary School, North Newton

# Dear Diary

Today, I felt excited because it was our first time at the Somerset Rural Life Museum.
For breakfast, I had Crunchy Nut cornflakes.
When I got to school, I went to the toilet, then I got my lunchbox and got in the minibus.
First, we played on the Smart Board, then I walked around the museum and made a magnet. I put my hand in the feely bags.
After, we went to the orchard and ate lunch.
Finally, we zoomed back to school.
Before bed, I brushed my teeth. What a lovely day I had!

**Katie Hunter (6)**

North Newton Community Primary School, North Newton

# Dear Diary

Today, I felt excited because we were going on a school trip.
When I got to school, I went to the toilet. Then I grabbed my lunch box and got on the minibus and drove to the museum.
First, we had a talk, then we played a game. We did some activities, then we had lunch. I had sandwiches, salt and vinegar crisps, a Cheestring, chocolate fingers and an apple. Then we played in the orchard. We drew an old tractor.
Before bed, I said goodnight to Mum. What a lovely day I had!

**Jenson Gair (7)**
North Newton Community Primary School, North Newton

# Dear Diary

Today, I felt excited because I went to Butlins. I went swimming with my mummy, daddy and James. Then I went on the Master Blaster with Daddy and the slide was blue. I went back to the flat with Mummy and Daddy and James. We had a shower and then we went on the helter-skelter. I went on my own. When I went on the swings on my own, I was very brave! Finally, I went on the go-karts with Mummy, Daddy and James. We all had fun!

**Daisy Hurford (6)**

North Newton Community Primary School, North Newton

# Dear Diary

Today, I felt happy because it was our class trip. I had Rice Krispies for breakfast. They were yum.
When I got to school, I got my lunch. First, I had a talk with Sandy. Then I made a magnet from sheep's wool.
After that, we had lunch. I had tuna sandwiches.
Finally, I went back to school. Before bed, I had a bath.

**Ella Loader (5)**
North Newton Community Primary School, North Newton

# Dear Diary

Today, I felt excited because it was our school trip to the museum. I had Rice Pops and a cup of water for breakfast.
When I got to school, I got my lunch box and got on the minibus and went to the museum.
First, we had to talk, then we made a fridge magnet. We felt bags. Then we had a look around the museum.

**Malakai Pike (5)**
North Newton Community Primary School, North Newton

# Dear Diary

Today I was excited because it was our class trip. I went to the museum.
First, we had a talk about what was in the museum and then we went to see.
Finally, we drove back to school.

**Isaac James Hadley (5)**
North Newton Community Primary School, North Newton

# Dear Diary

Today, I went to Disneyland with my family.
First, we went to our caravan and got dressed.
When we were walking, we saw little lizards with long tails.
When we got there, there were lots of big swimming pools that were very big and cool.
After that, I got some chips that they called crisps.
Finally, we went back to the caravan.

**Macey Cudmore (7)**
Pelynt Academy, Pelynt

# Dear Diary

Today, I went to the funfair with my best friends called Jessica and Macey. I went swimming with Jess and Macey. Me and Macey dressed as mermaids. We had lots of fun. We all went in the hot tub.
After an hour, we went to get cotton candy, then we all went home and played.

**Ellie Beal (7)**
Pelynt Academy, Pelynt

# Dear Diary

On Saturday, I went to Flambards. The first thing I did was go on the amazing roller coaster. I was enjoying myself, then the roller coaster broke! Suddenly, I had an idea. My plan was to climb to the end of the roller coaster. So I snuck on and made it safely to the end.

**Jasmine Goddard (6)**
Pelynt Academy, Pelynt

# Dear Diary

Two weeks ago, I went to Cedella's house. When I got there, we made slime. Unfortunately, it turned out as gloop. Then a rabbit jumped out of our video game! We chased after it. Suddenly, it jumped into the gloop and vanished!

**Ruby O'Keeffe (6)**
Pelynt Academy, Pelynt

# Dear Diary

Two weeks ago, my friend came over to my house. She is called Ruby. We made slime. First, we put special water in, then we put slime in and finally, we put in cornflower. It looked like a big, gooey mess!

**Cedella Secker (6)**
Pelynt Academy, Pelynt

# Dear Diary

Yesterday was the most exciting day of my life. First, we went to the beach. Next, Dad got the boat. After that, we went sailing, then we went to Millendreath Beach. Finally, we went home.

**William Beal (7)**
Pelynt Academy, Pelynt

# Dear Diary

On a sunny morning, I woke up. I was so excited because this was the day of my dreams. But first, I had to eat. I didn't need to take food with me. It was time to go to Candy Land! My parents were coming too. We ate half of a house that was completely made of sweet and sugary candy. There was some healthy stuff to eat too. We played lots of fun games. We stayed there for two hours.
When the two hours were over, we went home. We ate dinner, a healthy dinner. We watched TV all snuggled up on the comfy sofa. We watched the movie 'Back to the Future'. I love that movie. We had some popcorn, then I went to my big, comfy, snuggly bed and slept all through the night, dreaming of the adventure in Candy Land!

**Indigo Tookey-Moram (7)**
Plymouth School Of Creative Arts, Milbay

# Dear Diary

I woke up and got out of my fluffy bed. I got a shower, ready for school. It was like a hot tub! I got dry and got dressed in my lovely gown. Afterwards, I went to the bathroom on the left-hand side to brush my teeth really carefully because I have a wobbly tooth. Next, I walked down the stairs into the kitchen to have some breakfast. I had some Weetabix and a hot cross bun. It was very yummy!
I looked for my shoes, then I found them, finally. I put them on. They are red Converse. I put on my coat. My coat is a sparkly pink one, I got it from a shop in town. I put my drink in my bag and went to school.

**Phoebe Nottage (6)**
Plymouth School Of Creative Arts, Milbay

# Dear Diary

I woke up and I was excited because I knew
I was going on an adventure to the funfair. I
looked in my wardrobe and saw a monster!
I thought I could take him to the funfair
with me. He said, "Please, please, please!" I
asked him what his name was. I didn't
understand what he said. He spoke
differently to humans. He said, "Oooh gogo
lalala!"
We went to the funfair together. We had
lots of fun there. We went on the slides and
bouncy castles. I asked, "How old are you?"
I don't know what the answer was!
We went home together and now live
happily.

**Freya Cottam (7)**
Plymouth School Of Creative Arts, Milbay

# Dear Diary

Today, I went to school. I woke up. I ate my breakfast, brushed my teeth and got dressed to go to school. I got my hat and gloves on and my coat.
I got to school and I saw a big monster doing something. The monster helped me do my maths! People were running, then they stopped and were working.
I like my school, it is the best school. It is a big school with so many people in it. The school is cool, it's a type of monster school. I learnt maths after the monster helped me. It was fun. I had my lunch, then I did some reading on the carpet, then I went back home.

**Oliver**
Plymouth School Of Creative Arts, Milbay

# Dear Diary

I woke up and I was excited because it was the last day of school! I ate my breakfast as fast as I could so I could get to school quickly. I got dressed quickly and ran down the stairs to get my coat, bag and shoes on. I pulled down the handle quickly and went to school with my best friend, Freya. We walked for one mile and finally got to school. I played with Freya for the morning. In the afternoon, we wrote and then we went to the after school club.
I went home and played and then I went to sleep for nine hours.

**Evelyn Chudley (6)**
Plymouth School Of Creative Arts, Milbay

# Dear Diary

I woke up today and it was a very funny day. I felt so happy. I walked down the stairs and went to eat my breakfast. It was banana bars with milk.
After that, I got dressed. I wore a pink and purple dress with lots of flowers on. I went out the door to meet my friend, Imogen, in the park.
Finally, we went to the beach. Luckily, I found treasure and mermaids! I had cold fizzy Pepsi and seven crunchy chocolate chip cookies. Also, I had a strawberry ice cream.

**Aaliyah Bella Cabanga Jago (6)**
Plymouth School Of Creative Arts, Milbay

# Dear Diary

I woke up and I was very excited to go to the fun park with my cat, Munchie. I got dressed in my good dress, then I was in the car going to the fun park with Munchie.
At the fun park, me and my cat went down the super good slide. When we went down the slide, we got lost and met a really pretty person who led us back. Then we had a really nice swing on the swings.
After that, we went on the see-saw. I went home and had tea. Now I am in my bed going to sleep!

**Élodie Dickinson (7)**
Plymouth School Of Creative Arts, Milbay

# Dear Diary

I went to Legoland with my pet hamster. Me and my hamster arrived in our cars.
When we got there, there was loads of Lego stuff. Me and my hamster were amazed by the Lego stuff. Me and my hamster went on a Lego monster truck. We went up high and over cars, up big ramps and crashed into monster trucks. Then we went down a big Lego slide. We went on a Lego T-rex, it was awesome.
Finally, we had a Lego ice cream and went home.

**Declan (6)**
Plymouth School Of Creative Arts, Milbay

# Dear Diary

I woke up on a sunny day and I was going
to the park.
At the park, I talked to my friend and I
brought my Pokémon, Pikachu.
After that, I ate meatballs and spaghetti for
lunch, then I played on the swing with my
friend. We played on the climbing frame,
then the trampoline, then the slide.
Finally, I went home and played on my PS4.

**Jake Brown (7)**
Plymouth School Of Creative Arts, Milbay

# Dear Diary

I got up and I got dressed. I was so excited. I couldn't wait, so I got in the car with my fluffy pet unicorn and went to the park. When we got there, we went down the steep slide with a soft sandpit at the end. Me and my pet unicorn were having a picnic, we had some apple pie. Me and my pet unicorn went home and had some dinner.

**Rudi Lilly (7)**
Plymouth School Of Creative Arts, Milbay

# Dear Diary

Today I went to Everything Land! First, I got out of bed and got dressed. Next, I ate a big bowl of cereal quickly, then I drove there in a monster truck.
When I got there, I started fighting a lion! I was so bursting for the toilet that I peed! I couldn't pull my pants back up because they were glued to the floor!

**Arlo Zephyr Christie (6)**
Plymouth School Of Creative Arts, Milbay

# Dear Diary

I woke up in my bed. It was Sunday. It was a yellow, burning, sunny day. I met my friend, funny Harry. We went to the big fair, then we went to play a ball game. We played other games. It was fun. We won lots of soft, cuddly teddy bears. Yay!
Lastly, we had some delicious, scrumptious, chocolate ice cream. Yummy!

**Paris Reshid (7)**
Plymouth School Of Creative Arts, Milbay

# Dear Diary

I got out of bed sneakily. I then had my Fruit Loops quietly. After that, I brushed my teeth well. I brushed my hair loudly. I then went to the monkey tree.
After that, I went swimming with my friend, then I went home and had a midnight feast.
I had a pepperoni pizza and then I watched TV.

**Bella McCosh (7)**
Plymouth School Of Creative Arts, Milbay

# Dear Diary

I woke up and got dressed. My big brother and I went outside, I liked it.
I went to the funfair, my friend Iris came with me.
I had lots of fun.
I went back home and then I went to the movies, I watched 'Smallfoot'. I saw lots of yetis! I loved it.

**Blake Logan Chafer (7)**
Plymouth School Of Creative Arts, Milbay

# Dear Diary

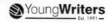

I woke up excitedly because I knew it was
the day I was going to go swimming.
I jumped into the water. I swam ten feet. I
swam like a turtle and it took lots of
practice because I swam in the deep water.
I drove home quickly. My dinner was
yummy.

**George James Mawdsley (6)**
Plymouth School Of Creative Arts, Milbay

# Dear Diary

I had a lovely day at the beach. It was sunny. I played on the rocks with my family. I went swimming with my dad. I had dinner with my family, then I went home.
In the morning, we went to the fairground and went on lots of things.

**Harry Adam South (7)**
Plymouth School Of Creative Arts, Milbay

# Dear Diary

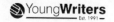

I got out of bed, then I got dressed in my favourite clothes. Next, I had a waffle for breakfast, then I went to the zoo. I saw a stripy tiger. Next, we got ice cream, then we went home and played games.

**Emi Hopkinson (6)**
Plymouth School Of Creative Arts, Milbay

# Dear Diary

I went to the football club and I played a game. Then I went to Woodlands and I went on really fun rides.
After that, I went back home and played video games. I went to bed and then I fell asleep.

**Zach Charlton (6)**
Plymouth School Of Creative Arts, Milbay

# Dear Diary

I woke up early in my bed. I had a warm shower and got dressed. I went to the scary woods with Mila and Freya.
When we got there, we were scared. Then I found a pebble! I went home.

**Sophia Styles (7)**
Plymouth School Of Creative Arts, Milbay

# Dear Diary

I got out of bed and went downstairs. I went to the zoo. I saw an elephant. I also saw a cool alligator. Then I had lunch. I ate mint ice cream. I had a lovely day and lots of fun.

**Rex Forest Mattess Nemeth (7)**
Plymouth School Of Creative Arts, Milbay

# Dear Diary

I woke up and got dressed. I got my space gear on. I got into my rocket and then I flew to the moon. I explored and I saw a UFO!

**Dylan Heddle (7)**
Plymouth School Of Creative Arts, Milbay

# Dear Diary

I went to the park today. It was amazing. I went with my family. Joshua (my brother), Mummy, Daddy and Basil, my dog. Our cousin, Joanna, is staying with us so we took her too. We went on all the equipment. My favourite part was going on the surfboard. I went very high and had to hold on tight!

Dear Diary,
Today we took our dog for a nice, long walk. We walked to the shops and Joanna took a look at the abbey. She thought it was beautiful and said how lucky we were. We then went into the Old Bell Hotel for a drink. Joanna is going home tomorrow. I can't wait until we can go and stay with her next time. She lives by the beach in Cornwall!

**Maisie Young-Weeks (7)**
St Joseph's Catholic School, Malmesbury

# Dear Diary

My name is Ben. I have a normal life but my adventures are different, so here is one of them...
One day, me and my dad went on a ride. I went on my skateboard so my dad went on his bike. I saw a rock so I jumped over it but at that moment, Dad disappeared and I was somewhere completely different! I ended up at a fair. I was riding a horse. I looked behind me. I'd had a feeling someone or something was following me. It was black and orange and so fluffy. I looked forward again. This time, I saw a castle in the distance. It looked extremely small from where I was. I got off the horse because I felt sick. I started to walk towards the castle. The rides were free. I looked, there were over a hundred rides to chose from! So close to being at the castle, I had a wonderful feeling about all of this but most of all, I wanted to know what was following me. Just then, the thing spoke.

It said, "Hi, I'm a tiger." And just at that moment, I was back with my dad.

**Esmie Butt (7)**
St Joseph's Catholic School, Malmesbury

# Dear Diary

I was snowboarding in the mountains when I was teleported to a hidden dragon world, which was covered in snow. A black dragon with red eyes as big as two vans chased me. I found a button. I pressed it and was teleported to the Minecraft dimension. I saw DanTDM. It was Christmas. I stayed in DanTDM's house for Christmas. It was epic. I loved it! I pressed a button and then I was back home.

**Olly Morris (7)**
St Joseph's Catholic School, Malmesbury

# Dear Diary

I am Suki the cat and I am Adeline's favourite teddy. I went to a farm with Adeline at the weekend. I got left behind. I felt scared and sad but then I had a fun adventure. I met the cows and sheep! I played with the dogs. I had a ride on the quad bike and on the big red tractor. I even climbed the big tree. The farmer then posted me home to Adeline.

**Adeline Andreou (5)**
St Joseph's Catholic School, Malmesbury

# Dear Diary

On Monday, I had a sleepover with a unicorn. It was so fun. I loved it. When we had the sleepover, we went to the playground to go on the swings. The unicorn was so good at swinging on the swings. Then we went back home and had some lunch. We played with my toys until it was tea, then we went to bed.
The next morning, we woke up and played in my bedroom. We played with Barbies. I showed the unicorn how to play with Barbies and then I cooked the dinner. We kept playing Barbies, then the unicorn went home. I closed the door. It was great having a unicorn around.

**Cecily Isabella King Dean (6)**
St Nicolas CE Primary School, Downderry

# Dear Diary

Last Thursday, I went to the aquarium for a sleepover with Year 2. First, I went home to pack and change. We quickly put my clothes in my suitcase and set off to the aquarium. When we got there, we learnt some things about fish, then we went to watch a movie. It was 'Zootropolis'. I wanted to watch that, and it won in voting.

We went to bed extremely late.

When we woke up, I had two breakfasts and they were delicious.

Finally, after breakfast, we went to the tunnel and saw sharks.

I loved it. I'd love to go again!

**Natalia Hoskins (7)**
St Nicolas CE Primary School, Downderry

# Dear Diary

Last week, I went to the United States of America.
When I was in America, I went to the Kennedy Space Centre.
I went inside the building and I saw a rocket! The rocket was as big as a plane.
I moved on and went to watch a movie.
When the movie was done, the screen lifted up and on the other side, there was a shuttle. It was the shuttle that was in the movie! Next to it was a play shuttle. I went inside it and there were loads of buttons. I then went to play in an international space station tunnel. I had a wonderful day!

**Parker Flood (7)**
St Nicolas CE Primary School, Downderry

# Dear Diary

In the winter holidays on Monday, I went to a rocket museum in London with my family, me, my brother, my mum and my dad. When we got there, we had to buy a ticket. We went to a room where the Pringle rocket shot in the air. It made me jump! We also saw controls. We got to move them, they connected to string so they moved! There was a remarkable, astonishing, infinity mirror. I put my head in it and I could see my head going round and round. I saw a colossal, huge, massive, gigantic rocket. That day was the best ever!

**Daisy Matthews (7)**
St Nicolas CE Primary School, Downderry

# Dear Diary

Last weekend, I went to Exmouth with my family for my seventh birthday. It was incredible there. There was a large swimming pool! It was really sunny and really hot so I went into the swimming pool to cool down with my family. After, we went into the caravan to have some dinner and a drink of Coke, but the Coke didn't have any sugar in so luckily, we didn't get poorly. Then we went to bed to get some sleep. It was so much fun in Exmouth.

**Eloise Manley (7)**
St Nicolas CE Primary School, Downderry

# Dear Diary

Last week, my friend came for a sleepover and we had a midnight feast. In the morning, we went downstairs and played a game. Then we went back upstairs, got dressed and went for breakfast. Our other friends came over and we made lemonade. We drank it, then we went outside to play. We played shops. We also went on the swing. It was a nice day. Then it was time to go home. I said bye, it was a good day and I wish it would happen again.

**Maya Walmsley (6)**
St Nicolas CE Primary School, Downderry

# Dear Diary

On Monday, I went to the park with my family. I went on the swing. I saw my friend. We went on the monkey bars and my baby brother went on the bars.
After that, we went to the shop and got stuff for our family. I bought things for my friend and my friend bought stuff for me. I bought Barbies and she bought Barbies. We went home and played Barbies. I have a big Barbie house so I was the mummy and Rose was the daughter.

**Daisy Prisk (7)**
St Nicolas CE Primary School, Downderry

# Dear Diary

Last week, I had a sleepover at my best friend, Maya's house. I played dominoes and with the doll's house. Also, we played a quick game of Twister. I had dinner and watched PAW Patrol.
After dinner, we slid down the stair handle, then we played on our Kindles. After that, we went to bed. We slept in the spare bedroom.
Finally, we had a yummy midnight feast!

**Willow Worthy (6)**
St Nicolas CE Primary School, Downderry

# Dear Diary

Last Easter, I went to Unicorn Land. When I was there, I went on a ride with my unicorn. When we got off, we got unicorn-shaped ice cream. Me and the unicorn went to the secret hideout. We went inside, there were creatures everywhere. We played for hours, then we went home. We played on the swing, then the unicorn went home. I said, "Goodbye!"

**Rosie Argyle (6)**
St Nicolas CE Primary School, Downderry

# Dear Diary

I went to France last winter. I went to a massive game and there was thunder and lightning when I was there. I slept in a gigantic, green tent.
In the night, when the wind blew, suddenly, the tent collapsed! We went to sleep in the van.
The next morning, we had to drive home. It was an hour and a half and when we got home, we had two power cuts!

**Isla Doyle (6)**
St Nicolas CE Primary School, Downderry

# Dear Diary

At the weekend, me, my sister's boyfriend and my sister went to get giant waffles in town.
When we went to town, we also got stuff for my family. It was sunny and it was a Saturday. First, we went to Drake's Circus. Then we got giant waffles. It was great.

**Edith Lloyd (7)**
St Nicolas CE Primary School, Downderry

# Dear Diary

I went on holiday with my family.
When I got there, we went to a spaceship. I got some food. After we got food, I went to my bedroom. It was dark.
When it was morning time, I had breakfast and a cup of milk.
Later, I went to my room to sleep.

**Abigail Matthews (5)**
St Nicolas CE Primary School, Downderry

# Dear Diary

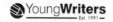

Last week, I went to the park with my mummy and daddy and sister and my unicorn teddy. I was very excited and I loved it.
When I was there, I went on the swing and the slide. I went with my unicorn on the helter-skelter. I went with my mummy.

**Autumn Manley (6)**
St Nicolas CE Primary School, Downderry

# Dear Diary

On Monday, I went to the funfair with my best friend and a monster. We went to the arcade and we played Mario Kart. Then we went into the café. I drank Pepsi and had pizza.
After that, we went home and watched TV.

**Theo Worthy (7)**
St Nicolas CE Primary School, Downderry

# Dear Diary

Last summer, I went to Denmark. We got on the train from Copenhagen to the ferry port. When we arrived at Samso Island off the coast of Denmark, it was late so we went to bed.
When we woke up, it was boiling hot!

**Miles Muller-Forster (6)**
St Nicolas CE Primary School, Downderry

# Dear Diary

Today, I went to the zoo. I went with my mum and cousins. We got to the car park and followed the map out of the car park. The first thing we saw was a tiger. After the tiger, we saw a lion. Then we saw the Komodo dragon!

**Piran George Wiltshire (5)**
St Nicolas CE Primary School, Downderry

# Dear Diary

I went to Portugal. We had to drive for ten
hours until we got to the hotel.
When we got there, we went to the
reception but the person said we had to
wait for five hours!

**Frazer Wool (6)**
St Nicolas CE Primary School, Downderry

# Dear Diary

I went to Newquay Zoo with my mummy, auntie, grandad, nanny and my brother also came with us. Some of the animals started flying and the rest were dancing! This was strange but me and my brother had a feeling it was Professor Demonhead. We walked around the zoo. All the animals seemed to be under a spell. We noticed that a statue in the middle of the grounds looked a bit out of place. As we approached it, this man jumped down and ran. It was Professor Demonhead! We chased after him but the guard managed to stop him. He was made to put things right and then taken away by the police.
We enjoyed the rest of the day and won't forget it easily.

**Aston Reeve (7)**
Stowford School, Ivybridge

# Dear Diary

I had a day with a unicorn. We went to the beach, the unicorn was really, really happy but the lifeguard said, "No unicorns." The unicorn was sad, but me and the unicorn went to a unicorn and people beach. The beach was lots of fun. We played with each other. But there was a nasty dog and lady. The unicorn was scared and frightened, but I am a really good fighter so I made the mean lady and the dog go away.
We had a picnic, the unicorn had lots of fun with me and I had lots of fun with the unicorn. The unicorn was the nicest unicorn in the world.

**Ellie-Mae Iles (7)**
Stowford School, Ivybridge

# Dear Diary

I went to the park and met my friendly, nice friends. They are called Daisy and Blythe. We played on the hard, old swings and we played on everything else. It was so much fun. We had a blast. We were running all over the place. Suddenly, an ice cream van turned up and said, "Would you like ice cream?"
We said, "Yes please!" We loved it. It was so yummy. Once we'd had ice cream, we carried on playing.

**Evie Vickers (6)**
Stowford School, Ivybridge

# Dear Diary

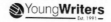

Over half-term, Mummy picked me up and then we drove to Looe. We stayed in a caravan with my family.
The next day, we went swimming underwater.
That evening, there was a disco in the clubhouse but I was too shy to dance.
The next day, we went to play in the arcades. I won lots of things.
On our last day, we went crabbing. We caught twenty-four crabs and I even held one. I had a great time.

**Teddy Hugo Ross (7)**
Stowford School, Ivybridge

# Dear Diary

I loved today because I went to my first ever hockey tournament. I saved quite a lot of goals. I was so good in goal. I kicked a lot of shots. Being a hockey goalie is harder than it looks. For a start, you have to put a huge bag full of kit on to protect you from being hurt. I am very proud of myself. We were against a team called Torbay. We only lost 2-0.

**Sebby Brown (7)**
Stowford School, Ivybridge

# Dear Diary

On Saturday, I went to Nanny and Grandad's house with my family. They live in Plymouth so it was a very long way to get there.
When we got there, we took our shoes off and gave Nanny a hug. We all sat on the sofa. Mum and Dad talked to my grandparents and then I asked if I could go and play upstairs. I made pictures for them.

**Evie Igoe (7)**
Stowford School, Ivybridge

YoungWriters®
Est. 1991

# Young Writers Information

We hope you have enjoyed reading this book – and that you will continue to in the coming years.

If you're a young writer who enjoys reading and creative writing, or the parent of an enthusiastic poet or story writer, do visit our website **www.youngwriters.co.uk**. Here you will find free competitions, workshops and games, as well as recommended reads, a poetry glossary and our blog. There's lots to keep budding writers motivated to write!

If you would like to order further copies of this book, or any of our other titles, then please give us a call or order via your online account.

Young Writers
Remus House
Coltsfoot Drive
Peterborough
PE2 9BF
(01733) 890066
**info@youngwriters.co.uk**

Join in the conversation!
Tips, news, giveaways and much more!